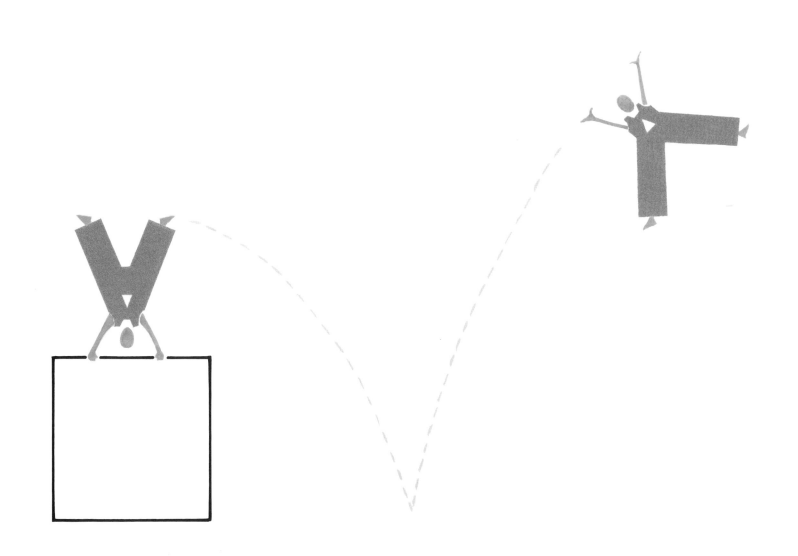

ALPHABATICS

Suse MacDonald

Aladdin Paperbacks

Aa

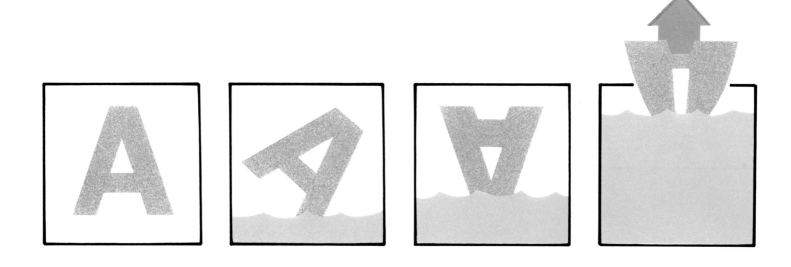

Ark

Bb

balloon

Cc

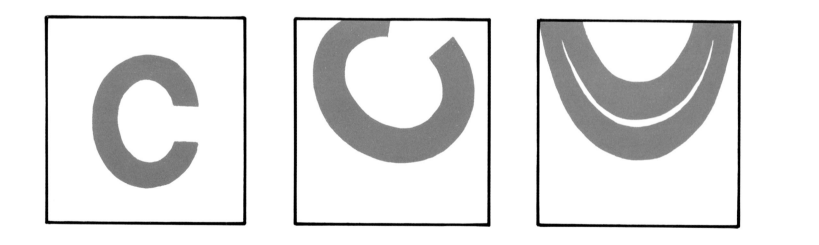

Clown

Dd

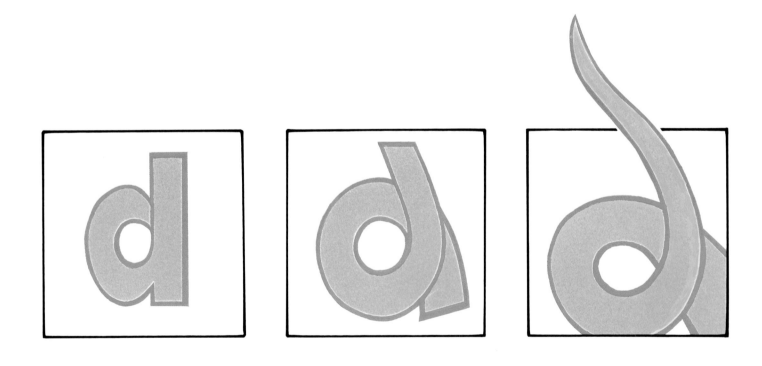

dragon

Ee

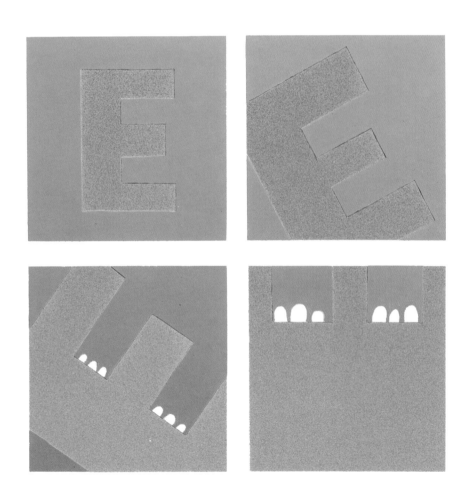

Elephant

Ff

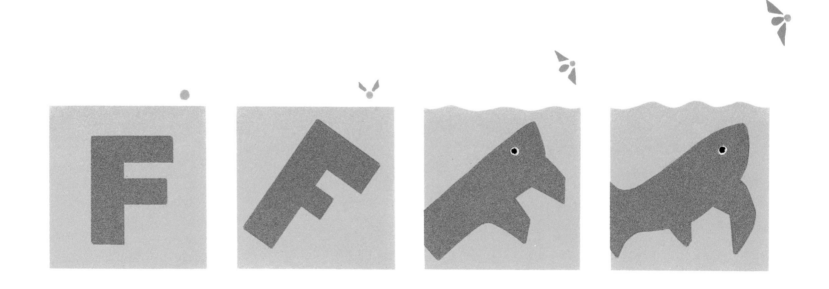

Fish

Gg

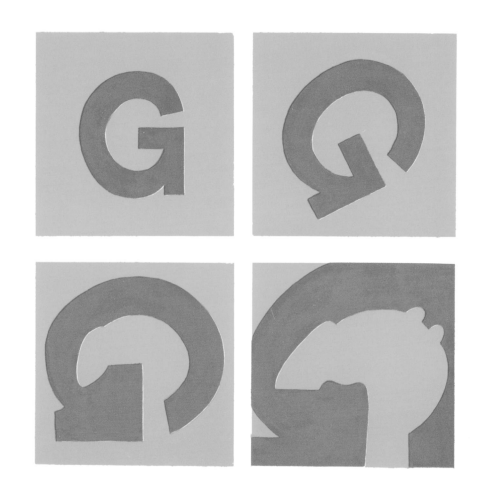

Giraffe

Hh

h

house

insect

Jj

jack-in-the-box

Kk

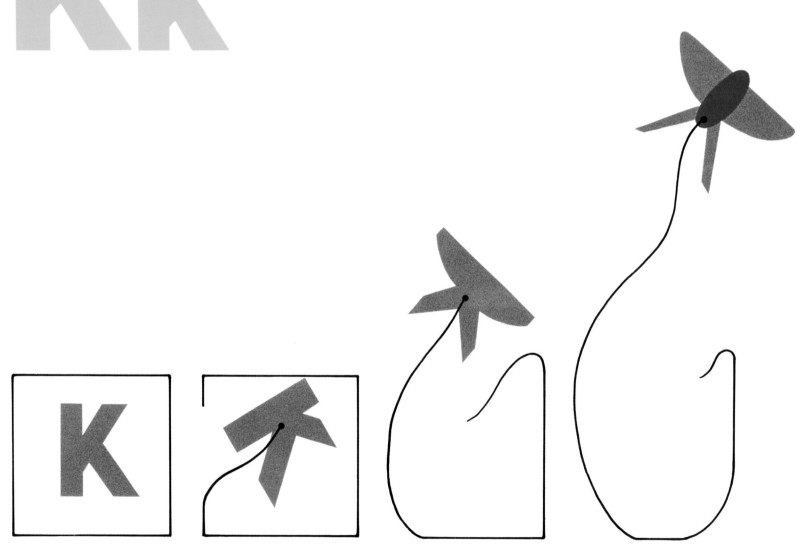

Kite

Ll

Lion

Mm

mustache

Nn

nest

Oo

owl

Plane

Qq

Quail

Rr

rooster

Ss

Swan

Tt

Tree

Uu

umbrella

Vv

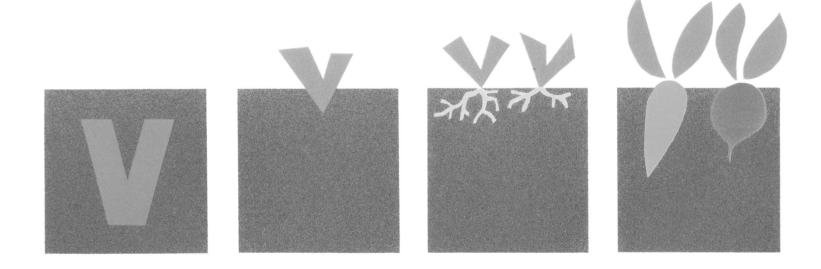

Vegetables

Ww

Whale

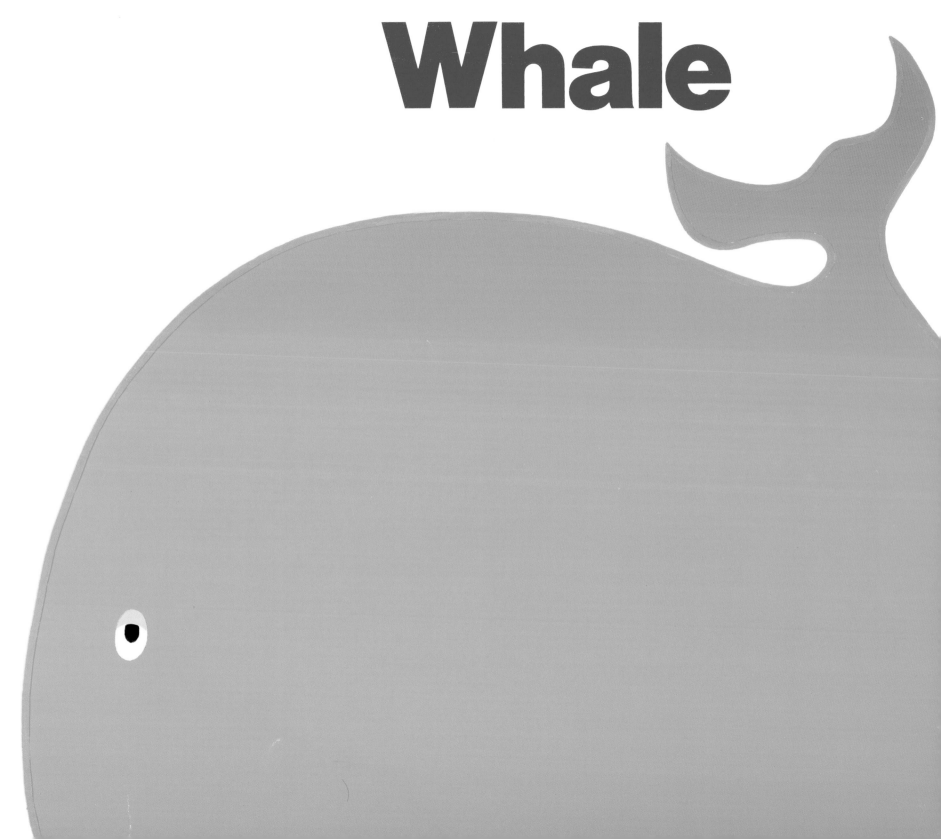

Xx

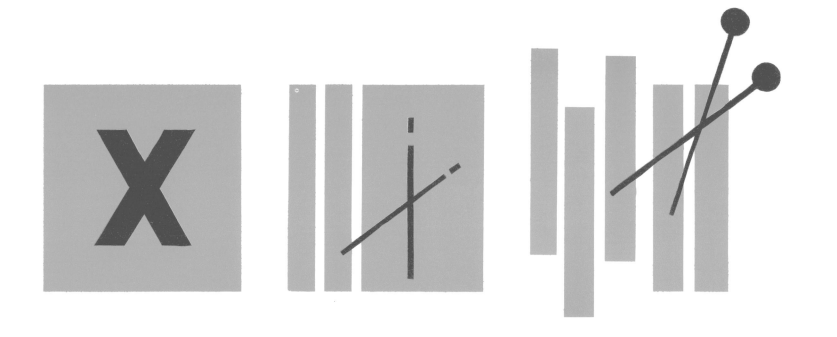

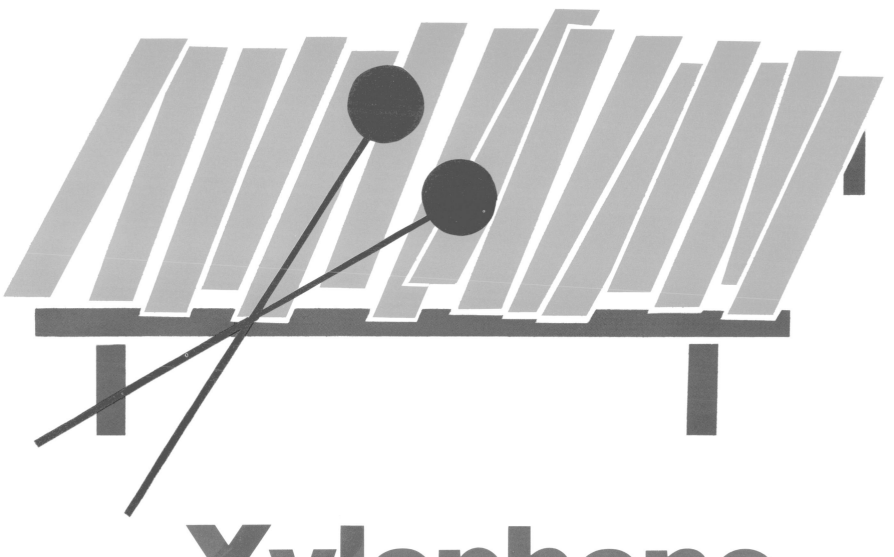

Xylophone

Yy

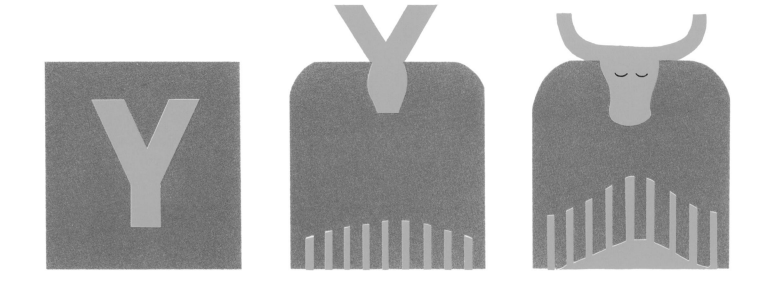

Yak

Zz

Zebra

For Stuart, with special thanks to Susan and Deborah

Aladdin Paperbacks. An imprint of Simon & Schuster Children's Publishing Division, 1230 Avenue of the Americas, New York, NY 10020. Copyright © 1986 by Suse MacDonald. All rights reserved including the right of reproduction in whole or in part in any form. First Aladdin Paperbacks edition, 1992. Also available in a hardcover edition from Simon & Schuster Books for Young Readers. Printed in Hong Kong. 10   9   8   7   6

Library of Congress Cataloging-in-Publication Data MacDonald, Suse. Alphabatics / by Suse MacDonald. — 1st Aladdin Books ed. p. cm. Originally published: New York : Bradbury Press, 1986. Summary: The letters of the alphabet are transformed and incorporated into twenty-six illustrations, so that the hole in "b" becomes a balloon and "y" turns into the head of a yak. ISBN 0-689-71625-7   1. English Language—Alphabet—Juvenile literature.   [1. Alphabet.] I. Title.   PE1155.M3   1992   [E]—dc20   91-38497